Christmas Tunes You've Always Wanted To Play

CHESTER MUSIC

(A division of Music Sales Ltd.)

8-9 Frith Street, London, W1V 5TZ
Exclusive distributors: Music Sales Ltd., Newmarket Road,
Bury St Edmunds, Suffolk, IP33 3YB

Exclusive Distributors: Music Sales Limited Newmarket Road, Bury St. Edmunds, Suffolk IP33 3YB
This book © Copyright 1999 Chester Music
ISBN 0-7119-7767-4
Order No. CH61632
Cover Design by Chloë Alexander

All Through The Night

Traditional

Angels From The Realms Of Glory

Traditional

With motion

1. An - gels from the realms of glo - ry, Wing your flight o'er all the earth;

Ye who sang cre - a - tion's sto - ry, Now pro - claim Mes - si - ah's birth:

Come and wor - ship, Come and wor - ship, Wor - ship Christ the new-born King!

2. Shepherds, in the fields abiding,
   Watching o'er your flocks by night,
   God with man is now residing,
   Yonder shines the infant Light:
   Come and worship, Come and worship,
   Worship Christ, the newborn King!

3. Sages, leave your contemplations,
   Brighter visions beam afar;
   Seek the great Desire of nations;
   Ye have seen His natal star:
   Come and worship, Come and worship,
   Worship Christ, the newborn King!

As With Gladness Men Of Old

Traditional

3. As they offered gifts most rare
   At that manger rude and bare,
   So may we with holy joy,
   Pure and free from sin's alloy,
   All our costliest treasures bring,
   Christ, to Thee, our heav'nly King.

4. Holy Jesus, every day
   Keep us in the narrow way;
   And, when earthly things are past,
   Bring our ransomed souls at last
   Where they need no star to guide,
   Where no clouds Thy glory hide.

Auld Lang Syne

Words by Robert Burns
Music: Traditional

Away In A Manger

Traditional

2. The cattle are lowing, the baby awakes,
   But little Lord Jesus no crying he makes,
   I love thee, Lord Jesus, look down from the sky,
   And stay by my side until morning is nigh.

3. Be near me, Lord Jesus, I ask thee to stay
   Close by me for ever, and love me, I pray:
   Bless all the dear children in thy tender care,
   And fit us for heaven, to live with thee there.

The Boar's Head Carol

Traditional

2. The boar's head as I understand,
    The bravest dish in all the land,
    When thus bedecked with a gay garland
    Let us *servire cantico.*
    (Let us serve with song.)
        Refrain

3. Our steward hath provided this
    In honor of the King of bliss,
    Which on this day to be served is,
    In reginensi atrio
    (In the royal hall.)
        Refrain

Carol Of The Drum

Words & Music by Katherine K. Davis

The Cherry Tree Carol

Traditional

2. When Joseph and Mary
   Walked through an orchard green,
   There were berries and cherries as thick as might be seen,
   There were berries and cherries as thick as might be seen.

3. And Mary spoke to Joseph,
   So meek and so mild,
   "Joseph, gather me some cherries for I am with child,
   Joseph, gather me some cherries for I am with child."

4. And Joseph flew in anger,
   In anger flew he,
   "Let the father of the baby gather cherries for thee,
   Let the father of the baby gather cherries for thee."

5. Then up spoke baby Jesus
   From in Mary's womb,
   "Bend down the tallest tree that my mother might have some,
   Bend down the tallest tree that my mother might have some."

6. And bent down the tallest branch
   'Til it touched Mary's hand,
   Cried she, "Oh, look thou Joseph, I have cherries by command,"
   Cried she, "Oh, look thou Joseph, I have cherries by command."

A Child This Day

Traditional

2. These tidings shepherds heard,
   In field watching their fold,
   Were by an angel unto them
   That night revealed and told:

   Nowell, Nowell, Nowell,
   Nowell, sing all we may,
   Because the King of all kings
   Was born this blessed day.

3. To whom the angel spoke,
   Saying, 'Be not afraid;
   Be glad, poor silly shepherds—
   Why are you so dismayed?

4. 'For lo! I bring you tidings
   Of gladness and of mirth,
   Which cometh to all people by
   This holy infant's birth':

5. Then was there with the angel
   An host incontinent
   Of heavenly bright soldiers,
   Which from the Highest was sent:

6. Lauding the Lord our God,
   And his celestial King;
   All glory be in Paradise,
   This heavenly host did sing:

7. And as the angel told them,
   So to them did appear;
   They found the young child, Jesus Christ,
   With Mary, his mother dear:

Christ Was Born On Christmas Day

Traditional

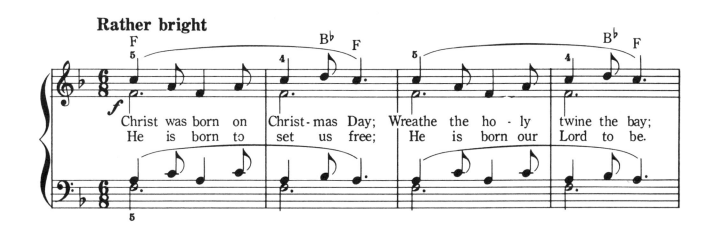

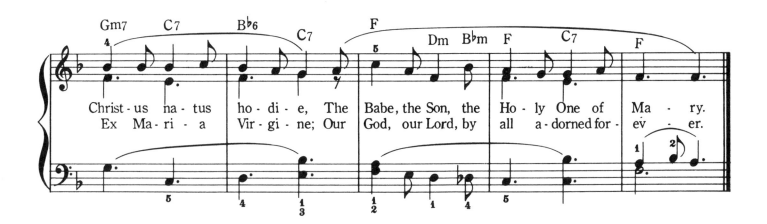

Christians Awake

Traditional

Lively, with spirit

1. Christ-ians, a-wake, sa-lute the hap-py morn, Where-on the Sa-viour of man-kind was born; Rise to a-dore the mas-ter-y of love, Which hosts of an-gels chant-ed from a-bove; With them the joy-ful tid-ings first be-gun Of God In-car-nate and the Vir-gin's Son.

2. Then to the watchful shepherds it was told,
Who heard th'angelic herald's voice: "Behold,
I bring good tidings of a Saviour's birth
To you and all the nations upon earth;
This day hath God fulfilled His promised word,
This day is born a Saviour, Christ, the Lord.

3. He spake, and straightway the celestial choir,
In hymns of joy, unknown before conspire:
The praises of redeeming love they sang,
And heav'n's whole arch with Alleluias rang,
God's highest glory was their anthem still,
Peace upon earth, and unto men good will.

Christmas Is Coming

Traditional

Moderately

① Christ - mas is com - ing! The goose is get - ting fat;

② Please to put a pen - ny in an old man's — hat,

③ Please to put a pen - ny in an old man's — hat.

Coventry Carol

Traditional

2. Herod, the king,
   In his raging,
     Chargèd he hath this day
   His men of might,
   In his own sight,
     All young childrén to slay.

3. That woe is me,
   Poor child for thee!
     And ever morn and day,
   For thy parting
   Neither say nor sing
     By by, lully, lullay!

Come All Ye Shepherds

Traditional

2. Come hear what wonderful tidings are fraught.
   In Bethlehem see what joy they have brought.
   Good will from heaven to man is given,
   Peace never ending to earth descending,
   Glory to God!

3. Haste then to Bethlehem, there to behold
   Jesus the Babe of whom angels have told.
   There to His glory tell we the story,
   Glad voices raising Him over praising,
   Hallelujah!

Deck The Halls

Traditional

2. See the blazing Yule before us,
Fa-la-la-la-la, la-la-la-la.
Strike the harp and join the chorus,
Fa-la-la-la-la, la-la-la-la.
Follow me in merry measure,
Fa-la-la, la-la la, la-la-la.
While I tell of Yuletide treasure,
Fa-la-la-la-la, la-la-la-la.

3. Fast away the old year passes,
Fa-la-la-la-la, la-la-la-la.
Hail the new, ye lads and lasses,
Fa-la-la-la-la, la-la-la-la.
Sing we joyous all together,
Fa-la-la, la-la la, la-la-la.
Heedless of the wind and weather.
Fa-la-la-la-la, la-la-la-la.

Ding Dong Merrily On High

Traditional

Ding dong! mer-ri-ly on high___ in heav'n the bells are ring - ing:
Ding dong! ve-ri-ly the sky___ is riv'n with An - gels sing - ing.

G   Am   D Em D G   C G Am7 D7   G

Glo - - - - - - - - - - -

D G   C D   B   Em   A   D

- - - - ri-a, Ho-san-na in ex-cel-sis!

G C G   D G D G   C G D   G

2. E'en so here below, below,
   Let steeple bells be swungen,
   And *i-o, i-o, i-o,*
   By priest and people sungen.
   Gloria, Hosanna in excelsis!

3. Pray you, dutifully prime
   Your Matin chime, ye ringers;
   May you beautifully rime
   Your Evetime Song, ye singers:
   Gloria, Hosanna in excelsis!

The First Nowell

Traditional

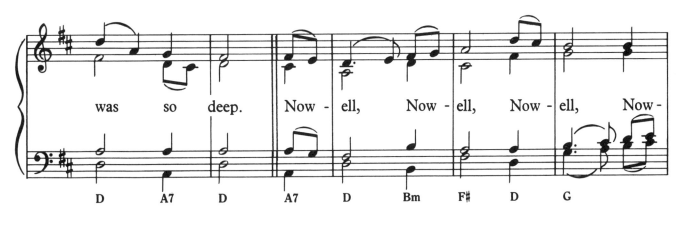

was so deep. Now - ell, Now - ell, Now - ell, Now -

D   A7   D   A7   D   Bm   F#   D   G

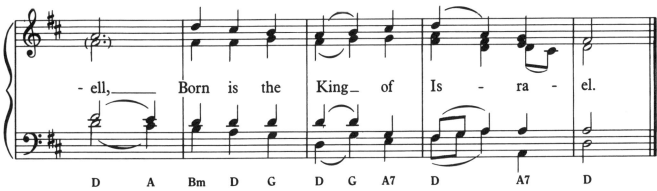

- ell,_____ Born is the King_ of Is - ra - el.

D   A   Bm   D   G   D   G   A7   D   A7   D

2. They lookèd up and saw a Star,
   Shining in the East, beyond them far,
   And to the earth it gave great light,
   And so it continued both day and night.
                    Nowell, etc.

3. And by the light of that same Star,
   Three Wise Men came from country far;
   To seek for a King was their intent,
   And to follow the Star wherever it went.
                    Nowell, etc.

4. This star drew nigh to the north-west,
   O'er Bethlehem it took its rest,
   And there it did both stop and stay,
   Right over the place where Jesus lay.
                    Nowell, etc.

5. Then entered in those Wise Men three,
   Full reverently upon their knee,
   And offered there, in His Presence,
   Their gold, and myrrh, and frankincense.
                    Nowell, etc.

6. Then let us all with one accord,
   Sing praises to our Heavenly Lord,
   That hath made Heaven and earth of nought,
   And with His Blood mankind hath bought.
                    Nowell, etc.

The Friendly Beasts

Traditional

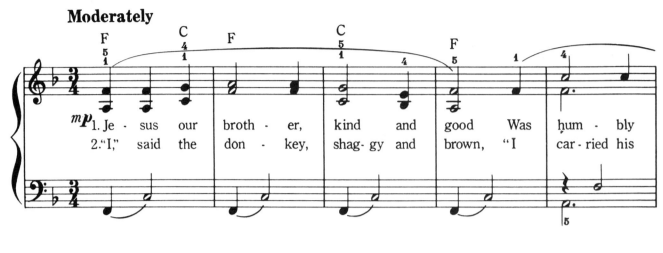

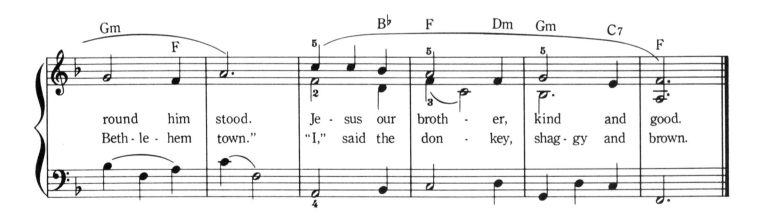

3. "I", said the cow all white and red,
   "I gave him my manger for his bed,
   I gave him my hay to pillow his head",
   "I", said the cow all white and red.

4.. "I", said the sheep with curly horn,
   "I gave him my wool for his blanket warm;
   He wore my coat on Christmas morn".
   "I" said the sheep with curly horn.

5. "I", said the dove from the rafters high,
   "Cooed him to sleep that he should not cry,
   We cooed him. to sleep, my mate and I",
   "I", said the dove from the rafters high.

6. Thus every beast by some good spell,
   In the stable dark was glad to tell
   Of the gift he gave Emanuel,
   The gift he gave Emanuel.

Fum, Fum, Fum

Traditional

Moderately, with marked rhythm

2. Thanks to God for holidays, sing fum, fum, fum.
Thanks to God for holidays, sing fum, fum, fum.
Now we all our voices raise — And sing a song of grateful
    praise,
Celebrate in song and story, all the wonders of his glory,
Fum, fum, fum.

God Rest You Merry Gentlemen

Traditional

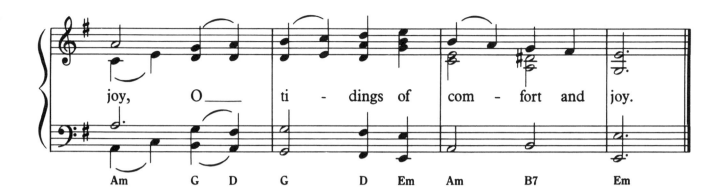

joy,   O____ ti - dings of com - fort and joy.

Am   G   D   G   D   Em   Am   B7   Em

2. In Bethlehem, in Jewry,
      This blessèd Babe was born,
   And laid within a manger,
      Upon this blessèd morn;
   The which His Mother Mary
      Did nothing take in scorn.
          O tidings, etc.

3. From God our Heavenly Father
      A blessed Angel came;
   And unto certain Shepherds
      Brought tidings of the same:
   How that in Bethlehem was born
      The Son of God by name.
          O tidings, etc.

4. "Fear not then," said the Angel,
      "Let nothing you affright,
   This day is born a Saviour
      Of a pure Virgin bright,
   To free all those that trust in Him
      From Satan's power and might."
          O tidings, etc.

5. The shepherds at those tidings
      Rejoicèd much in mind,
   And left their flocks a-feeding,
      In tempest, storm, and wind:
   And went to Bethlehem straightway,
      The Son of God to find.
          O tidings, etc.

6. And when they came to Bethlehem
      Where our dear Saviour lay,
   They found Him in a manger,
      Where oxen fed on hay;
   His Mother Mary kneeling down,
      Unto the Lord did pray.
          O tidings, etc.

7. Now to the Lord sing praises,
      All you within this place,
   And with true love and brotherhood
      Each other now embrace;
   This holy tide of Christmas
      All other do deface.
          O tidings, etc.

Good King Wenceslas

Traditional

2. 'Hither, page, and stand by me,
   If thou know'st it, telling,
   Yonder peasant, who is he?
   Where and what his dwelling?'
   'Sire, he lives a good league hence,
   Underneath the mountain,
   Right against the forest fence,
   By Saint Agnes' fountain.'

3. 'Bring me flesh, and bring me wine,
   Bring me pine-logs hither:
   Thou and I will see him dine,
   When we bear them thither.'
   Page and monarch, forth they went,
   Forth they went together;
   Through the rude wind's wild lament
   And the bitter weather.

4. 'Sire, the night is darker now,
   And the wind blows stronger;
   Fails my heart, I know not how;
   I can go no longer.'
   'Mark my footsteps, good my page;
   Tread thou in them boldly:
   Thou shalt find the winter's rage
   Freeze thy blood less coldly.'

5. In his master's steps he trod,
   Where the snow lay dinted;
   Heat was in the very sod
   Which the Saint had printed.
   Therefore, Christian men, be sure,
   Wealth or rank possessing,
   Ye who now will bless the poor,
   Shall yourselves find blessing.

The Golden Carol

Traditional

Moderately

mf

1. We saw a light shine out a-far, On Christ-mas in the morn - ing, And straight we knew it was Christ's star, Bright beam - ing in the morn - ing. Then did we fall on bend - ed knee, On Christ - mas in the morn - ing, And praised the Lord, who'd let us see, His glo - ry at its dawn - ing.

2. Oh! ever thought be of His name
    On Christmas in the morning,
    Who bore for us both grief and shame
    Affliction's sharpest scorning.
    And may we die when death shall come,
    On Christmas in the morning,
    And see in heav'n our glorious home,
    That star of Christmas morning.

Happy Xmas (War Is Over)

Words & Music by John Lennon & Yoko Ono

3. And so this is Xmas for weak and for strong
The rich and the poor ones the road is so long.
And so, happy Xmas for black and for white
For the yellow and red ones, let's stop all fights.
A merry, merry Xmas and a happy New Year.
Let's hope it's a good one without any fear.

Hark, The Herald Angels Sing

Words by Charles Wesley
Music by Felix Mendelssohn

2. Christ, by highest heaven adored,
   Christ, the everlasting Lord,
   Late in time behold him come,
   Offspring of a Virgin's womb,
   Veiled in flesh the Godhead see!
   Hail, the incarnate Deity!
   Pleased as Man with man to dwell,
   Jesus, our Emmanuel.
       Hark! the herald angels sing
       Glory to the new-born King.

3. Hail, the heaven-born Prince of Peace!
   Hail, the Sun of Righteousness,
   Light and life to all he brings,
   Risen with healing in his wings.
   Mild he lays his glory by,
   Born that man no more may die,
   Born to raise the sons of earth,
   Born to give them second birth.
       Hark! the herald angels sing
       Glory to the new-born King.

Have Yourself A Merry Little Christmas

Words & Music by Hugh Martin & Ralph Blane

Hear The Angel Voices

Traditional

The Holly And The Ivy

Traditional

3. The holly bears a berry
   As red as any blood,
   And Mary bore sweet Jesus Christ,
   To do poor sinners good:
   Refrain:

4. The holly bears a prickle,
   As sharp as any thorn,
   And Mary bore sweet Jesus Christ
   On Christmas day in the morn:
   Refrain:

The Holy City

Words by F.E Weatherly
Music by Stephen Adams

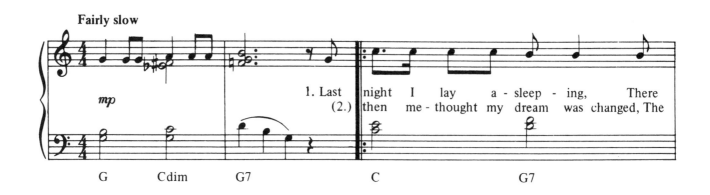

1. Last night I lay a-sleep-ing, There
(2.) then me-thought my dream was changed, The

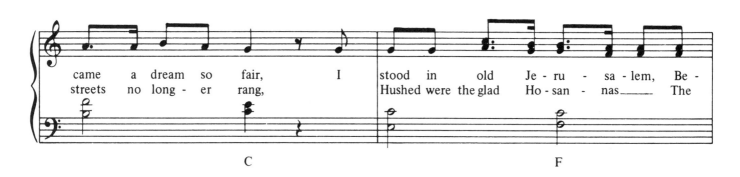

came a dream so fair, I stood in old Je - ru - sa - lem, Be -
streets no long - er rang, Hushed were the glad Ho - san - nas_____ The

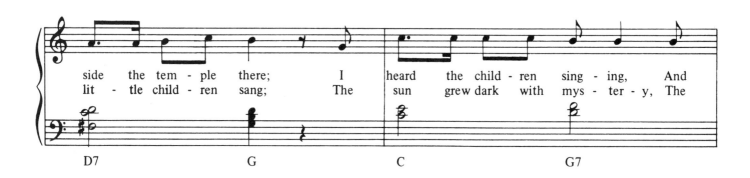

side the tem - ple there; I heard the chil - dren sing - ing, And
lit - tle chil - dren sang; The sun grew dark with mys - ter - y, The

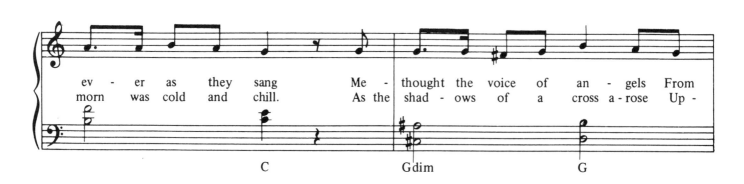

ev - er as they sang Me - thought the voice of an - gels From
morn was cold and chill. As the shad - ows of a cross a - rose Up -

earth there seemed to __ be, I saw the Ho-ly Ci-ty Be-side the tide-less sea; The

Am / E / C#m C7 E / B7 / E

light of God was on its streets, The gates were op-en wide, And all who would might

C#m / G#m / G / D / G / G7

en-ter, And no-one was de-nied. No need of moon or

C / F / C / G7 / C / Am / E

stars by night, Or sun to shine by day, It was the new Je-

Am / Am7 / F / Dm6 / C / C#dim

crescendo

Broadly

ru-sa-lem That would not pass a-way, It was the new Je-

G / D7 / G / D7 / G / D7

I Wonder As I Wander

Appalachian Carol

2. When Jesus was born, it was in a cow's stall,
With shepherds and wise men and angels and all.
The blessings of Christmas from heaven did fall,
And the weary world woke to the Savior's call.

I Believe In Father Christmas

Words by Peter Sinfield
Music by Greg Lake

Verse 2.

They sold me a dream of Christmas,
They sold me a silent night;
And they told me a fairy story
Till I believed in the Israelite
And I believed in Father Christmas,
And I looked to the sky with excited eyes,
Till I woke with a yawn in the first light of dawn,
And I saw him through his disguise.

Verse 3.

I wish you a hopeful Christmas
I wish you a brave New Year
All anguish, pain and sadness
Leave your heart and let your road be clear.
They said there'd be snow at Christmas
They said there'd be peace on earth
Hallelujah Noel be it heaven or hell
The Christmas we get we deserve.

I Saw Three Ships

Traditional

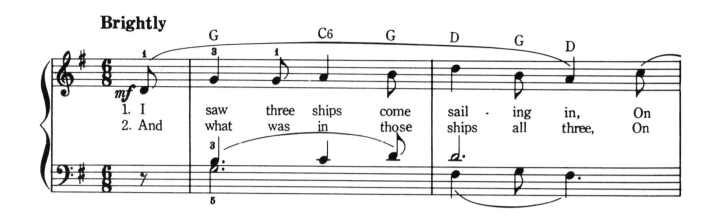

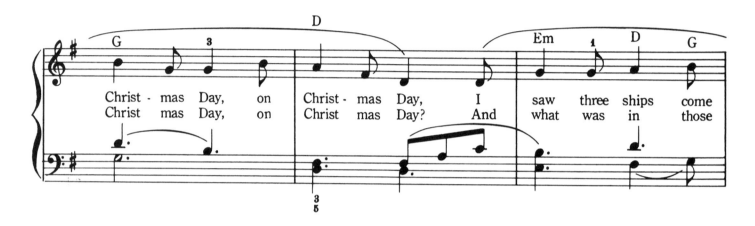

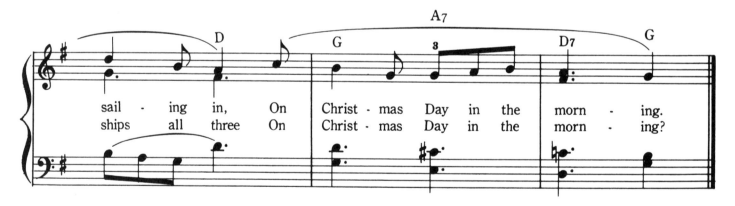

3. The Virgin Mary and Christ was there,
   On Christmas Day, on Christmas Day.
   The Virgin Mary and Christ was there,
   On Christmas Day in the morning.

4. Then let us all rejoice amain,
   On Christmas Day, on Christmas Day,
   Then let us all rejoice amain,
   On Christmas day in the morning.

In Dulci Jubilo

14th Century German Carol

2. *O Jesu, parvule,*
   For thee I long alway;
      Comfort my heart's blindness,
   O puer optime,
      With all thy loving-kindness,
   O princeps gloriae.
   Trahe me post te!

3. *O Patris caritas!*
   O Nati lenitas!
      Deeply were we stainèd
   Per nostra crimina;
      But thou for us hast gainèd
   Coelorum gaudia.
   O that we were there!

4. *Ubi sunt gaudia*
   In any place but there?
      There are angels singing
   Nova cantica,
      And there the bells are ringing
   In Regis curia.
   O that we were there!

Infant Holy

Traditional

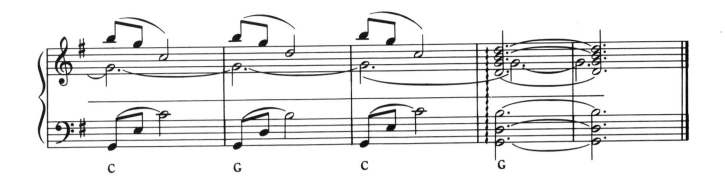

I Heard The Bells On Christmas Day

Words by Henry W. Longfellow
Music by J. Baptiste Colkin

1. I heard the bells on Christ-mas Day Their old fa - mil - iar car - ols play, And

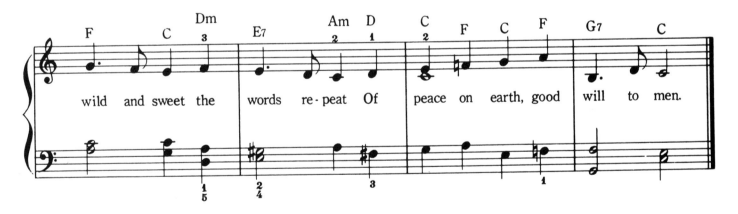

wild and sweet the words re - peat Of peace on earth, good will to men.

2. I thought how, as the day had come,
The belfries of all Christendom
Had rolled along th' unbroken song
Of peace on earth, good will to men.

3. And in despair I bowed my head,
"There is no peace on earth," I said,
" For hate is strong, and mocks the song
Of peace on earth, good will to men."

4. Then pealed the bells more loud and deep,
God is not dead, nor doth He sleep;
The wrong shall fail, the right prevail,
With peace on earth, good will to men.

5. Till, ringing, singing on its way,
The world revolv'd from night to day,
A voice, a chime, a chant sublime,
Of peace on earth good will to men.

It Came Upon The Midnight Clear

Words by Edmund Hamilton Sears
Music by Richard Storrs Willis

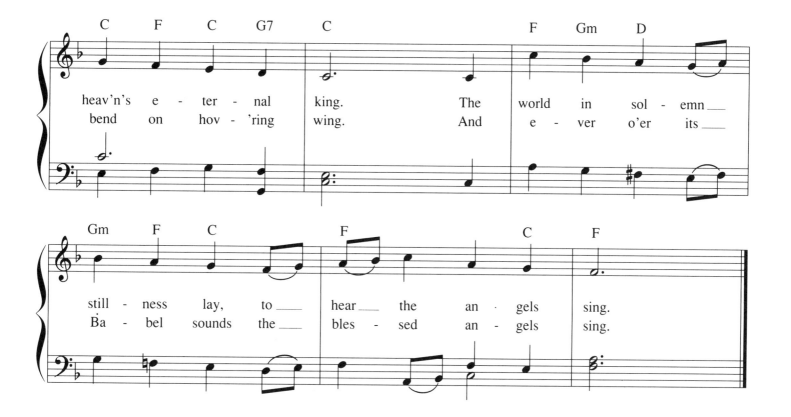

heav'n's e - ter - nal king. The world in sol - emn ___
bend on hov - 'ring wing. And e - ver o'er its ___

still - ness lay, to ___ hear ___ the an · gels sing.
Ba - bel sounds the ___ bles - sed an - gels sing.

3. Yet with the woes of sin and strife
   The world has suffered long;
   Beneath the angel-strain have rolled
   Two thousand years of wrong;
   And men, at war with men, hear not
   The love-song which they bring;
   Oh! hush the noise, ye men of strife
   And hear the angels sing!

4. And ye, beneath life's crushing load,
   Whose forms are bending low,
   Who toil along the climbing way
   With painful steps and slow,
   Look now! for glad and golden hours
   Come swiftly on the wing;
   O rest beside the weary road
   And hear the angels sing!

In The Bleak Mid-Winter

Words by Christina Georgina Rosetti
Music By Gustav Holst

In the bleak mid-win-ter Frost-y wind made moan,____

Earth stood hard as i-ron. Wa-ter like a stone;

Snow had fal-len snow on snow, Snow on____ snow,

In the bleak mid-win-ter, Long____ a-go.

2. God, heav'n cannot hold him,
   Nor earth sustain;
   Heav'n and earth shall flee away
   When he comes to reign.
   In the bleak mid-winter
   A stable place sufficed
   The Lord God Almighty,
   Jesus Christ.

3. Angels and archangels
   May have gathered there,
   Cherubim and seraphim
   Thronged the air –
   But his mother only,
   In her maiden bliss,
   Worshipped the Beloved
   With a kiss.

4. What can I give him,
   Poor as I am?
   If I were a shepherd
   I would bring a lamb;
   If I were a wise man
   I would do my part;
   Yet what I can I give him –
   Give my heart.

It's Gonna Be A Cold Cold Christmas

Words & Music by Roger Greenaway & Geoff Stephens

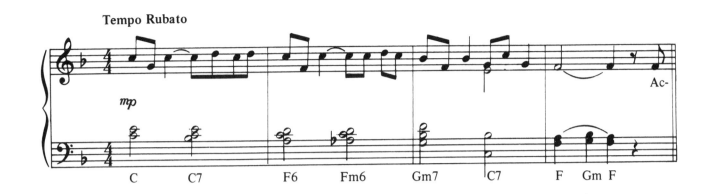

Ac-

-cord-ing to the ra - di - o warmer wea - ther's on the way and chan - ces are we won't be get-ting

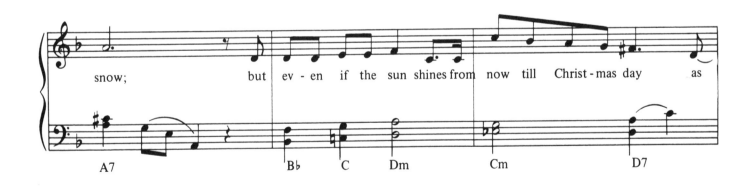

snow; but ev - en if the sun shines from now till Christ-mas day as

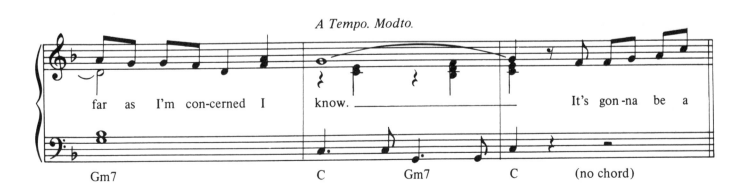

far as I'm con-cerned I know. _____ It's gon-na be a

INTERLUDE

1. Yes-ter-day I saw your Mum and Dad, _ we bought our cards to-geth-er,
2. I didn't bo-ther with the mis-tle toe, _ you won't be here to kiss me,

F   Am   Bb   C7

I've put the pre-sents on the Christ-mas tree _ and as I write this
The on-ly con-so-la-tion that I've got _ I know for sure you'll

F   Am   Bb

let - ter, it's warm _ in - side _ the
miss me; it won't _ be long _ un -

C7   Dm   F+

log - fire's burn - ing bright, oh dar - ling if on - ly you were
-til you're home a - gain, and we can _ share these ma - gic

F   Am7   D7   Gm

D.S. al fine

3

here to make it right. _ It's gon-na be a
moments but till then. _

Bbm   C7   (no chord)

55

Jingle Bells

Words & Music by J.S. Pierpont

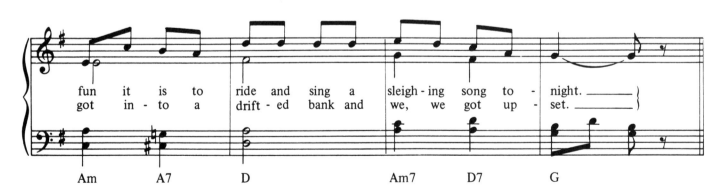

CHORUS

Jin - gle bells! Jin - gle bells! Jin - gle all the way!

(G)   C   G

Oh! what fun it is to ride in a one-horse op - en sleigh! Oh,

C   G   A7   D7

Jin - gle bells! Jin - gle bells! Jin - gle all the way!

G   C   G

Oh, what fun it is to ride in a one-horse op - en sleigh!

C   G   D7   G

3.   Now the ground is white,
     Go it while you're young!
     Take the girls tonight,
     And sing this sleighing song.
     Just get a bobtail'd bay,
     Two forty for his speed,
     Then hitch him to an open sleigh
     And crack! You'll take the lead.
               Chorus:

Joy To The World

Traditional

Majestically

2. Joy to the world! the Saviour reigns;
Let men their songs employ;
While fields and floods, rocks, hills and plains
Repeat the sounding joy,
Repeat the sounding joy,
Repeat, repeat the sounding joy.

3. He rules the world with truth and grace,
And makes the nations prove
The glories of His righteousness,
And wonders of His love,
And wonders of His love,
And wonders, and wonders of His Love.

Last Christmas

Words & Music by George Michael

Last Christ - mas I gave you my heart, __ but the ve - ry next day you gave it a - way. __

This year __ to save me from tears __ I'll give it to some - one spe - cial.

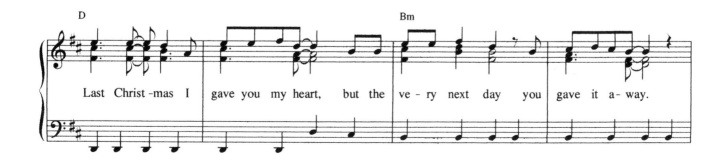

Last Christ -mas I gave you my heart, but the ve - ry next day you gave it a- way.

This year_ to save me from tears I'll give it to some-one spe - cial.

Once bit-ten and twice shy_____ I keep my dis-tance but

A crowd -ed room, friends with tir -ed eyes I'm hid - ing from you

you still catch my eye._ Tell me ba - by do you re-cog -nise me?

andyour soul_ of ice. My God! I thought_ you were some one to re - ly on.

Well, it's been a year, it doesn't surprise me (Happy Christmas!) I
Me? I guess I was a shoul-der to cry_ on. A face on a lo-ver with a

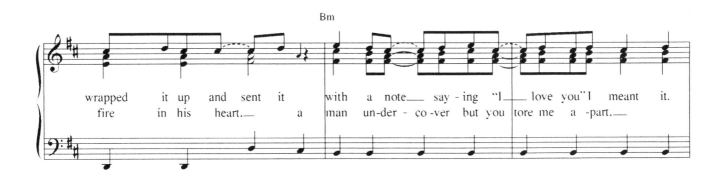

wrapped it up and sent it with a note_ say-ing "I_ love you"I meant it.
fire in his heart._ a man un-der-co-ver but you tore me a-part._

Now_ I know_ what a fool_ I've been_ but if you
now I've

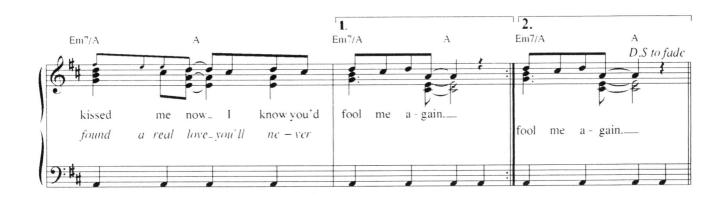

kissed me now_ I know you'd fool me a-gain._ fool me a-gain._
found a real love_you'll ne-ver

Let There Be Peace On Earth

Words & Music by Sy Miller and Jill Jackson

March Of The Three Kings

Provencal Melody

Mary Had A Baby

Traditional

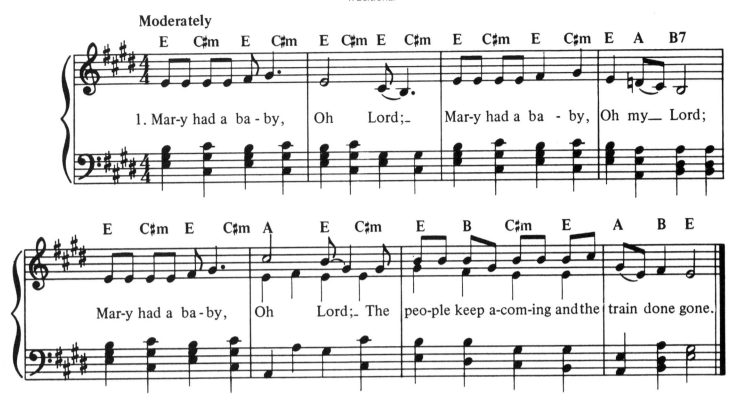

2. What did she name him, Oh, Lord?
   What did she name him, Oh, my Lord?
   What did she name him, Oh, Lord?
   The people keep a-comin' and the train done gone.

3. She called him Jesus, Oh, Lord,
   She called him Jesus, Oh, my Lord;
   She called him Jesus, Oh, Lord,
   The people keep a-comin' and the train done gone.

4. Now where was he born, Oh, Lord?
   Where was he born, Oh, my Lord?
   Where was he born, Oh, my Lord?
   The people keep a-comin' and the train done gone.

5. Born in a stable, Oh, Lord,
   Born in a stable, Oh, my Lord;
   Born in a stable, Oh, Lord,
   The people keep a-comin' and the train done gone.

6. Where did they lay him, Oh, Lord?
   Where did they lay him, Oh, my Lord?
   Where did they lay him, Oh, Lord?
   The people keep a-comin' and the train done gone.

7. Laid him in a manger, Oh, Lord,
   Laid him in a manger, Oh, my Lord;
   Laid him in a manger, Oh, Lord,
   The people keep a-comin' and the train done gone.

8. Who came to see him, Oh, Lord?
   Who came to see him, Oh, my Lord?
   Who came to see him, Oh, Lord?
   The people keep a-comin' and the train done gone.

9. Shepherds came to see him, Oh, Lord,
   Shepherds came to see him, Oh, my Lord;
   Shepherds came to see him, Oh, Lord,
   The people keep a-comin' and the train done gone.

10. The wise men kneeled before him, Oh, Lord,
    The wise men kneeled before him, Oh, my Lord;
    The wise men kneeled before him, Oh, Lord,
    The people keep a-comin' and the train done gone.

11. King Herod tried to find him, Oh, Lord,
    King Herod tried to find him, Oh, my Lord;
    King Herod tried to find him, Oh, Lord,
    The people keep a-comin' and the train done gone.

12. They went away to Egypt, Oh, Lord,
    They went away to Egypt, Oh, my Lord,
    They went away to Egypt, Oh, Lord,
    The people keep a-comin' and the train done gone.

13. Angels watching over him, Oh, Lord,
    Angels watching over him, Oh, my Lord;
    Angels watching over him, Oh, Lord,
    The people keep a-comin' and the train done gone.

Masters In this Hall

Traditional

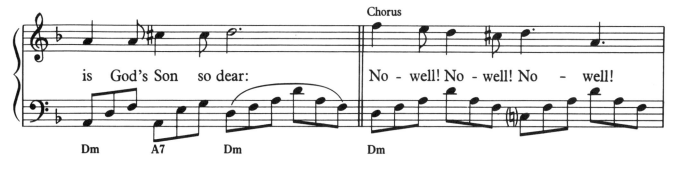

is God's Son so dear:

Chorus

No - well! No - well! No - well!

Dm   A7   Dm   Dm

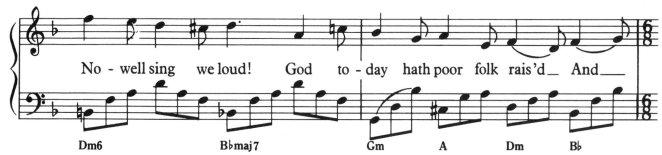

No - well sing we loud! God to - day hath poor folk rais'd— And—

Dm6   B♭maj7   Gm   A   Dm   B♭

Fine

cast a - down the proud.

Dm   A7   Dm   F   B♭   A   Dm

2. Going o'er the hills;
   Thro' the milk-white snow,
   Heard I ewes bleat
   While the wind did blow.

3. Shepherds many an one
   Sat among the sheep,
   No man spake more word
   Than they had been asleep.

4. Quoth I, "Fellows mine,
   Why this guise sit ye?
   Making but dull cheer
   Shepherds tho' you be?"

5. "Shepherds should of right
   Leap and dance and sing,
   Thus to see ye sit,
   Is a right strange thing."

6. Quoth those fellows then,
   "To Bethlem Town we go,
   To see a Mighty Lord
   Lie in manger low."

7. "How name ye this Lord
   Shepherds?", then said I
   "Very God," they said,
   "Come from Heaven high."

8. Then to Bethlem Town
   We went two and two,
   And in a sorry place
   Heard the oxen low.

9. Therein did we see
   A sweet and goodly May
   And a fair old man,
   Upon the straw She lay.

10. And a little Child
    On Her arm had She
    "Wot ye Who This is?",
    Said the hinds to me.

11. Ox and ass Him know,
    Kneeling on their knee,
    Wondrous joy had I
    This little Babe to see.

12. This is Christ the Lord,
    Masters be ye glad!
    Christmas is come in,
    And no folk should be sad.

Merry Christmas Everybody

Words & Music by Neville Holder & James Lea

3. Are you hanging up a stocking on your wall?
   Are you hoping that the snow will start to fall?
   Do you ride on down the hillside in a buggy you have made?
   When you land upon your head then you bin slayed;

Mistletoe And Wine

Words by Leslie Stewart & Jeremy Paul
Music by Keith Strachan

dreams   of   snow,   Fin - gers   numb,   fa - ces a -

glow. It's   Christ - mas   time,   mis-tle toe and wine,

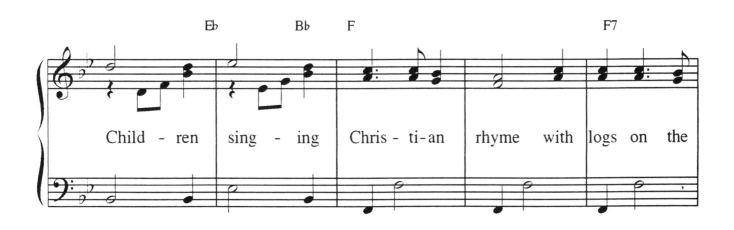

Child - ren   sing - ing   Chris - ti - an   rhyme with logs on the

fire__ and   gifts on the tree   A   time to re - joice in the

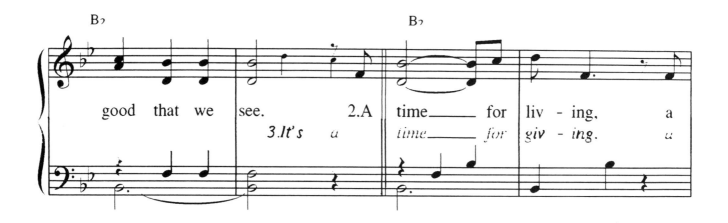

good that we see.　2.A time＿ for liv - ing, a
3.It's a time＿ for giv - ing. a

time for be - liev - ing, A time＿ for trust - ing,
time for get - ting, A time for＿ for - giv - ing,

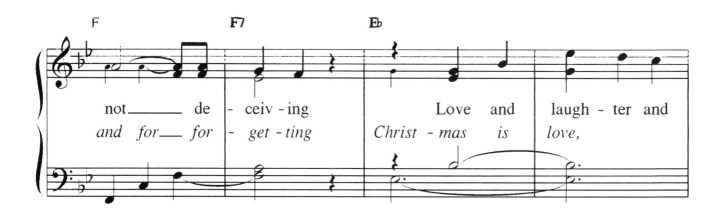

not＿ de - ceiv - ing Love and laugh - ter and
and for＿ for - get - ting Christ - mas is love,

joy ev - er af - ter; Ours for the tak - ing just fol - low＿ the
Christmas is＿ peace; A time for hat - ing and fight - ing＿ to

mas - ter. cease. Christ - mas time,

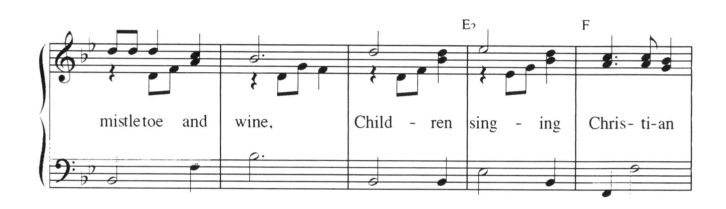

mistletoe and wine, Child - ren sing - ing Chris - ti-an

rhyme with logs on the fire__ and gifts on the tree; A

time to re - joice in the good that we see. see.

O Come All Ye Faithful

Words & Music by John Francis Wade
English words by Frederick Oakeley

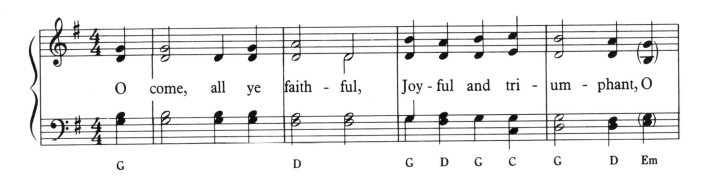

O come, all ye faith - ful, Joy - ful and tri - um - phant, O

come__ ye, O come__ ye to Beth - le - hem;

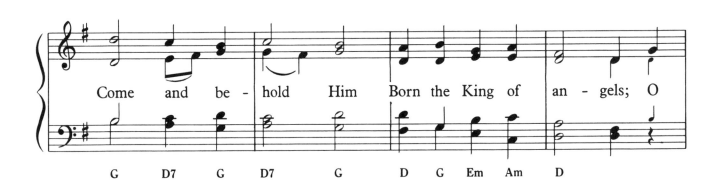

Come and be - hold Him Born the King of an - gels; O

come, let us a - dore Him, O come, let us a - dore Him, O

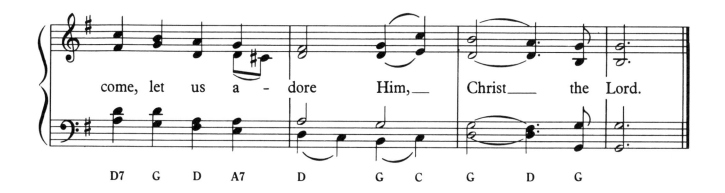

come, let us a - dore Him, ___ Christ ___ the Lord.

D7 G D A7 D G C G D G

2. God of God,
   Light of light,
   Lo! He abhors not the Virgin's womb;
   Very God,
   Begotten not created;

   O come, let us adore Him,
   O come, let us adore Him,
   O come, let us adore Him,
   Christ the Lord.

3. Sing, choirs of angels,
   Sing with exultation,
   Sing, all ye citizens of heaven above,
   Glory to God
   In the highest!

4. Yea, Lord, we greet Thee,
   Born this happy morning;
   Jesu, to Thee be glory given;
   Word of the Father,
   Now in flesh appearing;

O Christmas Tree (O Tannenbaum)

Traditional

2. ‖: O Christmas Tree, O Christmas Tree,
   Thy message is enduring; :‖
   So long ago in Bethlehem
   Was born the Saviour of all men;
   O Christmas Tree, O Christmas Tree,
   Thy message is enduring.

3. ‖: O Christmas Tree, O Christmas Tree,
   Thy faith is so unchanging; :‖
   A symbol sent from God above,
   Proclaiming Him the Lord of Love;
   O Christmas Tree, O Christmas Tree,
   How true you stand unchanging!

O Little Town Of Bethlehem

Words by Phillips Brooks
Music by Lewis Redner

3. How silently, how silently,
   The wondrous gift is giv'n!
   So God imparts to human hearts
   The blessing of his heav'n.
   No ear may hear His coming,
   But in this world of sin,
   Where meek souls will receive Him still,
   The dear Christ enters in.

4. O Holy Child of Bethlehem!
   Descend to us, we pray;
   Cast out our sin, and enter in;
   Be born in us today.
   We hear the Christmas angels
   The great glad tidings tell;
   O come to us abide with us,
   Our Lord Emmanuel.

O Come, O Come Emmanuel

Traditional

Refrain

Re - joice! Re - joice! Em - man - u - el shall come to thee, O Is - ra - el.

2. O come, Thou Wisdom from on high,
   And order all things, far and nigh;
   To us the path of knowledge show,
   And cause us in her ways to go.
   Refrain

3. O come, Desire of nations, bind
   All peoples in one heart and mind;
   Bid envy, strife, and quarrels cease;
   Fill the whole world with heaven's peace.
   Refrain

4. O come, Thou Day-spring, come and cheer
   Our spirits by Thine advent here;
   Disperse the gloomy clouds of night,
   And death's dark shadows put to flight.
   Refrain

O Saviour Sweet

Words & Music J.S. Bach

Gently moving

1. O Saviour sweet, O Saviour kind, Who all men's hearts in love did bind. O send from heav'n Thy tender care, That we may for Thy throne prepare. O Saviour sweet, O Saviour kind.

2. O Saviour meek, O Saviour mild,
   Who came a happy Christmas Child,
   Good will and peace and heavenly light
   Came to all men that blessed night.
   O Saviour meek, O Saviour mild.

3. O God of grace, O God of love,
   Thy blessings send us from above;
   Protect us from all earthly strife,
   And guide us to Thy perfect Life.
   O God of grace, O God of love.

Once In Royal David's City

Words by Cecil Alexander
Music by Henry Gauntlett

2. He came down to earth from heaven
   Who is God and Lord of all,
And his shelter was a stable,
   And his cradle was a stall;
With the poor and mean and lowly
Lived on earth our Saviour holy.

3. And through all his wondrous childhood
   He would honour and obey,
Love and watch the lowly Maiden,
   In whose gentle arms he lay:
Christian children all must be,
Mild, obedient, good as he.

4. And our eyes at last shall see him,
   Through his own redeeming love,
For that Child so dear and gentle
   Is our Lord in heaven above;
And he leads his children on
To the place where he is gone.

5. Not in that poor lowly stable,
   With the oxen standing by,
We shall see him; but in heaven,
   Set at God's right hand on high;
Where like stars his children crowned
All in white shall wait around.

Past Three O'Clock

Traditional

2. ℣. Seraph quire singeth,
   Angel bell ringeth:
   Hark how they rime it,
   Time it, and chime it. ℟

3. ℣. Mid earth rejoices
   Hearing such voices
   Ne'ertofore só well
   Carolling *Nowell*. ℟

4. ℣. Hinds o'er the pearly
   Dewy lawn early
   Seek the high stranger
   Laid in the manger. ℟

5. ℣. Cheese from the dairy
   Bring they for Mary,
   And, not for money,
   Butter and honey. ℟

6. ℣. Light out of star-land
   Leadeth from far land
   Princes, to meet him,
   Worship and greet him. ℟

7. ℣. Myrrh from full coffer,
   Incense they offer:
   Nor is the golden
   Nugget witholden. ℟

8. ℣. Thus they: I pray you,
   Up, sirs, nor stay you
   Till ye confess him
   Likewise, and bless him. ℟

Rise Up, Shepherd, And Follow

Spiritual Carol

Rocking

Traditional Czech Carol

2. Mary's little baby, sleep, sweetly sleep,
   Sleep in comfort, slumber deep;
      We will rock you, rock you, rock you,
      We will rock you, rock you, rock you:
   We will serve you all we can,
   Darling, darling little man.

A Rootin' Tootin' Santa Claus

Words & Music by Oakley Haldeman & Peter Tinturin

long lit tle rein -deer Git a - long:____ Cov - er all the range to- night.____ It's a

long, long trail,____ An all night trail_ But you can bet your boots that

San - ta won't fail: He's a Roo-t'n Too-t'n San - ta Claus.___ And he's on his mer-ry

way,____ He will round up all your Christ -mas dreams,____ with a

1.

yip - py - yo ki - ya!____ He's a

2.

Saviour's Day

Words & Music by Chris Eaton

Now we have been through the har- vest,

win- ter has tru- ly be-gun; now we are walk-ing the chill of the night, we are

wait-ing for, wait-ing for,___ for the Sa -viour's Day.

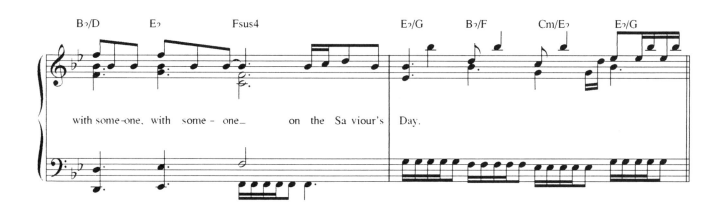

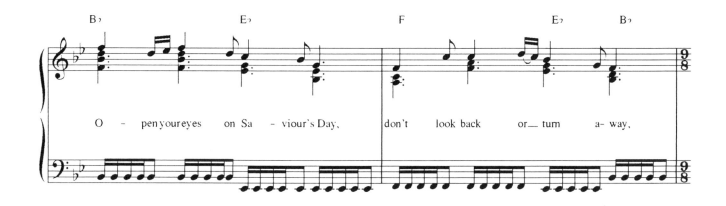

Day   on the Sa -viour's Day,   on the Sa -viour's

Day   He_____ is   call - ing___ you_   on the Sa -viour's
                                   on the Sa -viour's Day.

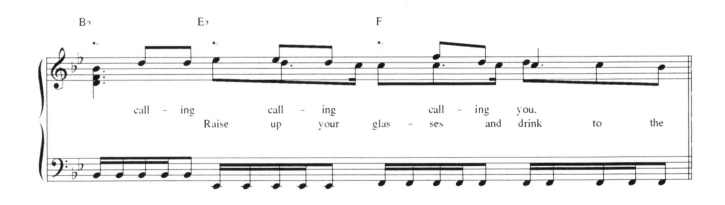

call - ing   call - ing   call - ing you.
Raise   up   your   glas - ses   and   drink   to   the

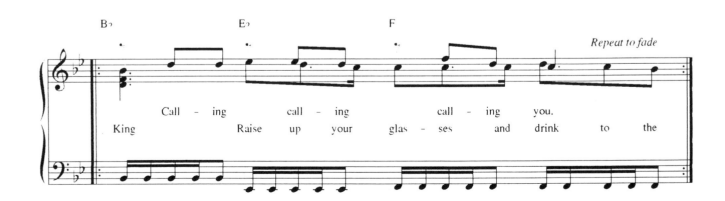

Repeat to fade

Call - ing   call - ing   call - ing you.
King   Raise   up   your   glas - ses   and   drink   to   the

92

See Amid The Winter's Snow

Words by Edward Caswall
Music by John Goss

See a-mid the win-ter's snow, Born for us on earth be-low,

G Am7 Bm C G G D C G G D

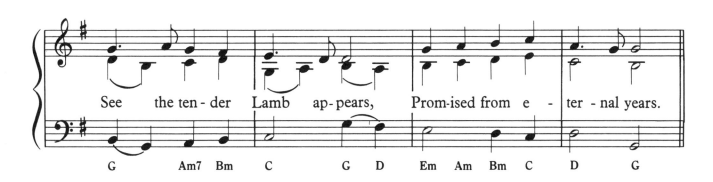

See the ten-der Lamb ap-pears, Prom-ised from e-ter-nal years.

G Am7 Bm C G D Em Am Bm C D G

Chorus:

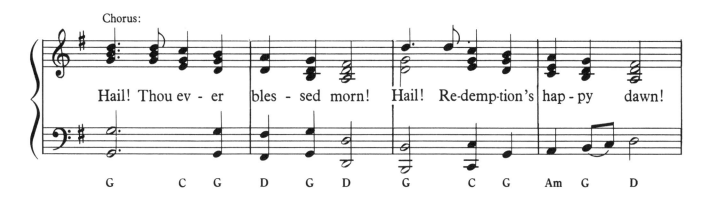

Hail! Thou ev-er bles-sed morn! Hail! Re-demp-tion's hap-py dawn!

G C G D G D G C G Am G D

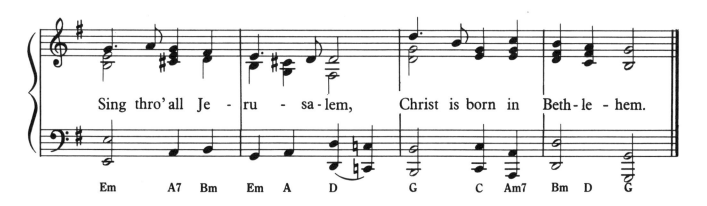

Sing thro' all Je-ru-sa-lem, Christ is born in Beth-le-hem.

Em A7 Bm Em A D G C Am7 Bm D G

2. Lo, within a manger lies
   He who built the starry skies;
   He, who throned in height sublime,
   Sits amid the Cherubim!
   Hail, thou ever-blessed, etc.

3. Say, ye holy Shepherds, say,
   What your joyful news to-day;
   Wherefore have ye left your sheep
   On the lonely mountain steep?
   Hail, thou ever-blessed, etc.

4. "As we watched at dead of night,
   Lo, we saw a wondrous light;
   Angels singing peace on earth,
   Told us of a Saviour's Birth."
   Hail, thou ever-blessed, etc.

5. Sacred Infant, all Divine,
   What a tender love was Thine;
   Thus to come from highest bliss
   Down to such a world as this!
   Hail, thou ever-blessed, etc.

6. Teach, O teach us, Holy Child,
   By Thy face so meek and mild,
   Teach us to resemble Thee,
   In Thy sweet humility!
   Hail, thou ever-blessed, etc.

Silent Night

Words by Joseph Mohr
Music by Franz Gruber

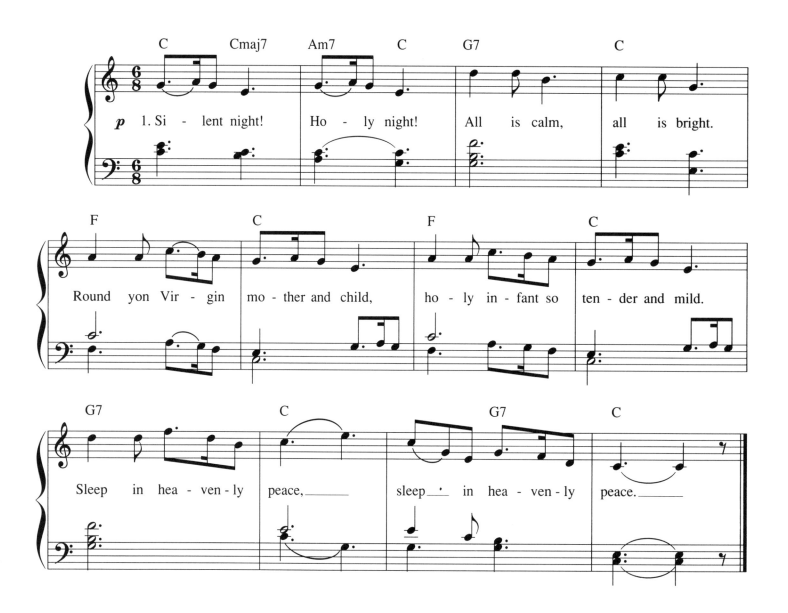

2. Silent night, holy night,
   Shepherds wake at the sight;
   Glory streams from heaven afar,
   Heavenly hosts sing Alleluia.
   Christ the Saviour is born!
   Christ the Saviour is born!

3. Silent night, holy night,
   Son of God, love's pure light;
   Radiance beams from Thy holy face,
   With the dawn of redeeming grace,
   Jesus, Lord at Thy birth,
   Jesus, Lord at Thy birth.

Sing, Shepherds!

Hungarian Carol

Song Of The Crib

Traditional German Carol

Men shall bring him from far and wide Love's di - a - dem; Je - sus,

Eb   Fm7   Bb11 Bb7 Eb   Gm   Cm

Je - sus, Lo, he comes, and Love's and saves, and frees us!

Gm   Cm   Ab   Gm   Fm   Bb11 Bb7   Ab   Eb

2. Gladly, dear one, lady mine,
   Help I cradle this child of thine;
   God's own light on us both shall shine
       In Paradise,
           As prays the mother Mary.

   Chorus:
   He came among us at Christmas tide,
       At Christmas tide,
           In Bethlehem;
   Men shall bring him from far and wide
       Love's diadem:
   Jesus, Jesus,
   Lo, he comes, and loves, and saves, and
                               [*frees us!*

3. *Servant* (1)
   Peace to all that have goodwill!
   God, who heaven and earth doth fill,
   Comes to turn us away from ill,
       And lies so still
           Within the crib of Mary.

4. *Servant* (2)
   All shall come and bow the knee;
   Wise and happy their souls shall be,
   Loving such a divinity,
       As all may see
           In Jesus, Son of Mary.

5. *Servant* (3)
   Now is born Emmanuel,
   Prophesied once by Ezekiel,
   Promised Mary by Gabriel—
       Ah, who can tell
           Thy Praises, Son of Mary!

6. *Servant* (4)
   Thou my lazy heart hast stirred,
   Thou, the Father's eternal Word,
   Greater than aught that ear hath heard,
       Thou tiny bird
           Of love, thou Son of Mary.

Sleigh Ride

Words by Mitchell Parish
Music by Leroy Anderson

We're rid-ing in a won-der-land of snow. ___ Gid-dy yap, gid-dy-yap, gid-dy yap, it's grand,

C#m   F#   B   Bm7   E

just hold-ing your hand, ___ We're glid-ing a-long with a song of a win-ter-y fair-y

A   C   D7   C

land; Our cheeks are nice and ro-sy, and com-fy co-zy are we, ___ We're snug-gled up to-ge-ther like two

D7   G   D7   G   D7   G

birds of a fea-ther would be. ___ Let's take that road be-fore us and sing a cho-rus or

D7   G   Bb   D7   G   D7

To Coda ⊕

two, ___ Come on, it's love-ly wea-ther for a Sleigh ride to-geth-er with you. ___ There's a

G   D7   G   D7   G

A Spaceman Came Travelling

Words & Music by Chris De Burgh

1.A space -man came trav -'ling on his ship from a-far, twas light years of time since his mis -sion did start and

ov-er a vil-lage he halt-ed his craft, and it hung in the sky like a

star just like a star

1,2,4.

3,5.

and it went la, la, la, la, la, la, la, la, la, la,

la, la, la, la, la, la la, la, la, la, la, la, la, la, la, la, la, la,

peace and good will to all men___ and love for the

child. La, la, la, la, la, la, la, la, la, la,

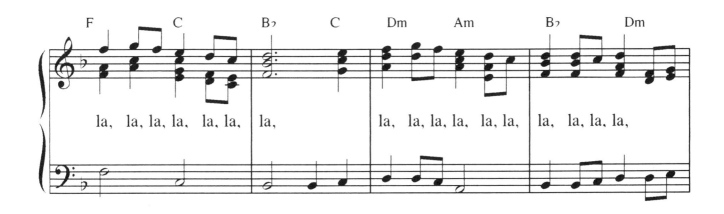

la, la, la, la, la, la, la, la, la, la, la, la, la, la, la, la, la,

To Coda ⊕   *D. 𝄋 al coda*

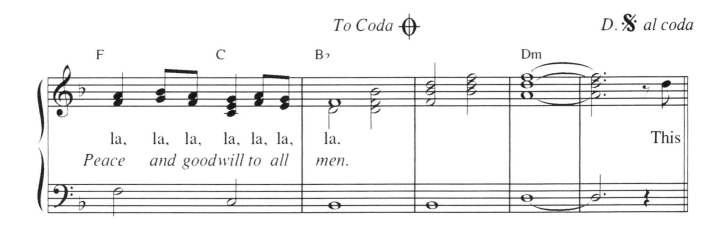

la, la, la, la, la, la, la.   This
Peace   and goodwill to all   men.

CODA

and love for the child. Oh the whole world is wait-ing

wait - ing for that song a - gain

there are thou -sands stand - ing on the edge of the world

and a star is mov-ing some -where, the time is near-ly here this

song will be - gin once a - gain

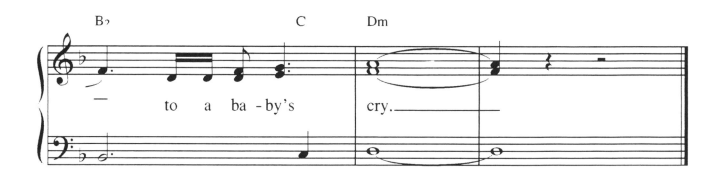

to a ba - by's cry.

Verse 2

He followed a light and came down to a shed
Where a mother and child were lying on a bed
A bright light of silver shone round his head,
And he had the face of an angel and they were afraid

Verse 3

Then the stranger spoke he said do not fear
I come from a planet a long way from here
And I bring a message for mankind to hear,
And suddenly the sweetest music filled the air.

Verse 4

This lovely music went trembling throught the ground
And many were wakened on hearing the sound
And trav'lers on the road the village they found
By the light of that ship in the sky which shone all around.

Verse 5

And just before dawn at the paling of the sky
The stranger returned and said now I must fly
When two thousand years of your time has gone by
The song will begin once again to a baby's cry.

Sussex Carol

Traditional

2. When sin departs before Thy grace,
   Then life and health come in its place;
   Angels and men with joy may sing,
   All for to see the new-born King. } *Repeat twice*

3. All out of darkness we have light,
   Which made the angels sing this night;
   "Glory to God and peace to men,
   Now and for evermore. Amen." } *Repeat twice*

The Twelve Days Of Christmas

Traditional

Unto Us A Boy Is Born

Traditional

2. Cradled in a stall was he
   With sleepy cows and asses;
   But the very beasts could see
   That he all men surpasses.

3. Herod then with fear was filled:
   'A prince', he said, 'in Jewry!'
   All little boys he killed
   At Bethl'em in his fury.

4. Now may Mary's son, who came
   So long ago to love us,
   Lead us all with hearts aflame
   Unto the joys above us.

5. Omega and Alpha he!
   Let the organ thunder,
   While the choir with peals of glee
   Doth rend the air asunder.

Up On The Housetop

Traditional

2. First comes the stocking of little Nell;
   Oh, dear Santa, fill it well;
   Give her a dollie that laughs and cries,
   One that will open and shut her eyes.
   Refrain:

3. Next comes the stocking of little Will;
   Oh, just see what a glorious fill;
   Here is a hammer and lots of tacks,
   Also a ball and a whip that cracks.
   Refrain:

Wassail Song

Traditional

2. Our wassail cup is made
   Of the rosemary tree,
   And so is your beer
   Of the best barley:

   Love and joy come to you,
   And to you your wassail too,
   And God bless you, and send you
   A happy new year.
   And God send you a happy new year.

3. We are not daily beggars
   That beg from door to door,
   But we are neighbours' children
   Whom you have seen before:

4. Call up the butler of this house,
   Put on his golden ring;
   Let him bring us up a glass of beer,
   And better we shall sing:

5. We have got a little purse
   Of stretching leather skin;
   We want a little of your money
   To line it well within:

6. Bring us out a table,
   And spread it with a cloth;
   Bring us out a mouldy cheese
   And some of your Christmas loaf:

7. God bless the master of this house,
   Likewise the mistress too;
   And all the little children
   That round the table go:

8. Good Master and good Mistress,
   While you're sitting by the fire,
   Pray think of us poor children
   Who are wandering in the mire:

We Three Kings

Words & Music by John Henry Hopkins

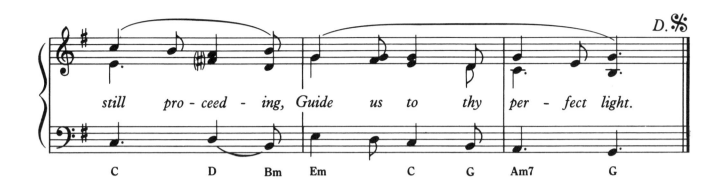

still pro - ceed - ing, Guide us to thy per - fect light.

C D Bm Em C G Am7 G

2. Born a king on Bethlehem plain,
   Gold I bring, to crown him again —
   King for ever, ceasing never,
   Over us all to reign:

   O star of wonder, star of night,
   Star with royal beauty bright,
   Westward leading, still proceeding,
   Guide us to thy perfect light.

3. Frankincense to offer have I;
   Incense owns a Deity nigh:
   Prayer and praising, all men raising,
   Worship him, God most high:

4. Myrrh is mine; its bitter perfume
   Breathes a life of gathering gloom;
   Sorrowing, sighing, bleeding, dying,
   Sealed in the stone-cold tomb:

5. Glorious now, behold him arise,
   King, and God, and sacrifice!
   Heaven sings alleluya,
   Alleluya the earth replies:

We Wish You A Merry Christmas

Traditional

2. Now bring us some figgy pudding,
   Now bring us some figgy pudding,
   Now bring us some figgy pudding,
   And bring some out here.

   Good tidings we bring
   To you and your kin,
   We wish you a Merry Christmas,
   And a Happy New Year.

3. For we all like figgy pudding,
   We all like figgy pudding,
   For we all like figgy pudding,
   So bring some out here.

4. And we won't go till we've got some,
   We won't go, till we've got some,
   And we won't go till we've got some,
   So bring some out here.

What Child Is This?

Traditional

Moderato

1. What Child is this who, laid to rest On Mar-y's lap, is sleep-ing? Whom an-gels greet with an-thems sweet, While shep-herds watch are keep-ing? This, this is Christ the King, Whom shep-herds guard and an-gels sing! Haste, haste to bring Him laud, The Babe, the Son of Mar-y!

2. Why lies He in such mean estate,
   Where ox and ass are feeding?
   Good Christian, fear: for sinners here,
   The silent world is pleading:
   Nails, spear, shall pierce Him through,
   The Cross be born, for me, for you:
   Hail, hail, the Word made flesh,
   The Babe, the Son of Mary!

3. So bring Him incense, gold and myrrh,
   Come peasant king to own Him,
   The King of kings, salvation brings,
   Let loving hearts enthrone Him.
   Raise, raise the song on high,
   The Virgin sings here lullaby:
   Joy, joy, for Christ is born,
   The Babe, the Son of Mary!

When Santa Got Stuck Up The Chimney

Words & Music by Jimmy Grafton

120

While Shepherds Watched

Traditional

While shep - herds watch'd their flocks by night,

F   F   C   Dm   B♭   F

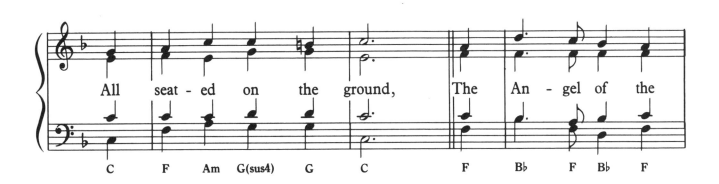

All seat - ed on the ground, The An - gel of the

C F Am G(sus4) G C   F B♭ F B♭ F

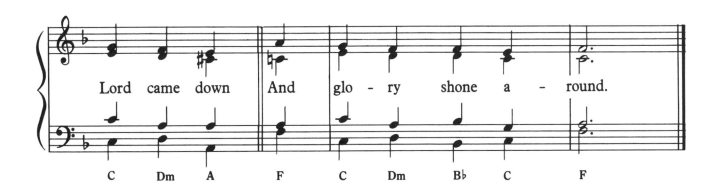

Lord came down And glo - ry shone a - round.

C Dm A   F C Dm B♭ C   F

2. "Fear not," said he; For mighty dread
   Had seized their troubled mind;
   "Glad tidings of great joy I bring
   To you and all mankind."

3. "To you in David's town this day
   Is born of David's line
   A Saviour, Who is Christ the Lord;
   And this shall be the sign:"

4. "The heavenly Babe you there shall find
   To human view display'd,
   All meanly wrapp'd in swathing bands,
   And in a manger laid."

5. Thus spake the seraph; and forthwith
   Appear'd a shining throng
   Of Angels praising God, who thus
   Address'd their joyful song:

6. "All glory be to God on high,
   And to the earth be peace;
   Good-will henceforth from heaven to men
   Begin and never cease."

Whence Is That Goodly Fragrance

Old French Carol

Translation A. B. Ramsay

1. Whence is that goodly fragrance flow-ing, Steal-ing our sens - es all a - way?____ Nev - er the like did come a -

blow - ing, Shep-herds, from flow - 'ry fields in May.___

Whence is that good - ly fra - grance flow - ing, Steal - ing our

sens - es all a - way?___ - way?___

2. What is that light so brilliant, breaking
   Here in the night across our eyes?
   Never so bright the day-star waking
   Started to climb the morning skies!
   What is that light so brilliant, breaking
   Here in the night across our eyes?

3. Bethlehem! there in manger lying
   Find your Redeemer, haste away!
   Run ye with eager footsteps hieing!
   Worship the Saviour born to-day!
   Bethlehem! there in manger lying
   Find your Redeemer, haste away!

Wonderful Christmas Time

Words & Music by Paul McCartney

Fairly bright four

The mood is right,

the spi-rit's up   we're here to-night

CODA

The choir of child-ren sing their song, they prac-tised all year long.

Ding, dong, ding, dong, ding, dong, ding, dong, ding, dong, ding, dong, ding, dong, ding, (dong).

The par-ty's on _____ the spi-rit's up _____
The mood is right, _____ *the spi -rit's up*

we're here to-night _____ and that's e - nough

Printed in Malta by Interprint Limited 7/01 (40823)